EXPRESSIVE SINGING

SONG ANTHOLOGY

$13.33

BROWN

MUSIC SERIES

Consulting Editor

FREDERICK W. WESTPHAL
Sacramento State College

Volume One

**Choice Basic Songs
For School or Studio**

Medium Voice Edition

EXPRESSIVE SINGING
SONG ANTHOLOGY

Selected, arranged, and edited by

Van A. Christy
University of California at
Santa Barbara

wcb

WM. C. BROWN COMPANY PUBLISHERS
Dubuque, Iowa

ISBN 0—697—03647—2

Library of Congress Catalog Card Number: M61-1027

Twenty-Fourth Printing, 1981

BOOKS IN THIS SERIES

EXPRESSIVE SINGING, VOLUME I
(*Basic Principles*)

EXPRESSIVE SINGING, SONG ANTHOLOGY, VOLUME I
(*High, Medium and Low Editions*)

EXPRESSIVE SINGING, VOLUME II
(*Correlated Advanced Theory, Technic, Pedagogy, and Repertoire*)

EXPRESSIVE SINGING, SONG ANTHOLOGY, VOLUME II
(*High, Medium and Low Editions*)

———

FOUNDATIONS IN SINGING
(*A Basic Textbook in the Fundamentals of Technic
and Song Interpretation*)

Printed in U. S. A.

Foreword

Although there is careful correlation between *Expressive Singing, Volume I TEXTBOOK* and the *Song Anthologies* in this complete vocal course, each may be used independently by those who wish to do so. However, beginning vocal students will find this *Song Anthology, Volume I*, ideal to accompany the theory of vocal production and vocal exercises in the first part of *Expressive Singing, Volume I TEXTBOOK* while intermediate and advanced students will discover that *Volume II Anthology* is equally suitable to integrate with the latter chapters of *Volume I TEXTBOOK*.

Most students will find in this beginning voice collection both ideal and ample vocal literature for one year of study. Voice Classes, or students desiring even easier beginning songs for initial study, or to supplement the vocal literature found in *Vol. I*, are urged to investigate *Foundations in Singing*, also published by the Wm. C. Brown Company. Those who are ready for more requiring songs, or to concentrate sooner on specific types of song literature such as Old English, Old Italian, German Lieder, French Impressionistic, etc., will find *Song Anthology, Vol. II* of this series unequalled for this purpose.

Needs of all voices, whether they be low, medium, or high, are accommodated in the three key editions (Low, Medium, and High Voice) published for the first time by any firm in an extensive song collection of this type. Although some beginning voice classes may prefer to start with the Low Key edition, the Medium Voice key edition will be found more practical for most ensemble classwork and for the majority of beginning students. Individual students whose voices are quite low, or high, should, after consultation with their instructor, select the edition that best suits their voice needs at the time.

Songs in this collection were selected carefully with four major objectives in mind: First, the vocal needs and interests of beginning students were considered of prime importance; second, only songs of artistic worth were included that would be of interest for concert programming; third, total content was chosen carefully to be certain that it included a varied and ample source of favorite song literature that experienced teachers have found of greatest value in developing the singing technic of beginning students; and fourth, attractiveness to both the student and teacher. We believe that the experienced teacher will find this song volume unequalled for the objectives stated.

Although all songs except the new ballad and folk song settings by the author have been concert favorites for many years, they are still within the capability of first year students to sing effectively. Vocal range is limited to an octave and a third in most instances, while no song demands more than an octave and a fifth. In addition, sustained tessitura was also given careful consideration before choosing just the right keys for the songs in each of the three voice editions. Piano scores are nearly all of an easy grade and will be found complete in introductions, interludes, and original composer content.

In order to provide maximum assistance to the student, specific suggestions in respect to style, mood, prevailing tone color and hints on interpretation of each song are provided in the Appendix. These should be read carefully before starting a song. Suggestions provided here and interpretive markings in the scores should be followed faithfully unless the teacher indicates a preference for variation. Songs are also edited carefully in more detail than usual in regard to dynamics, tempo and phrasing. Recommended length of phrases is marked with an apostrophe and, where needed for those with weak breath control, optional places are indicated with an encircled apostrophe.

Unusually wide variety of style and mood is represented within the twenty-two art songs, eight sacred songs, and spirituals, five humorous ballads, and ten folk songs in this volume. There are five optional duets, often interesting and useful to beginning students, and a generous representation of sacred songs and humorous ballads, often needed but usually slighted in collections for beginning students.

Song Anthology, Volume I, features songs in English. However, art songs composed originally with foreign language lyrics have this text included also for those desiring to sing in the original tongue. Rules for foreign language pronunciation of Italian, German and French will be found in the Appendix. Examination of English language translations provided will reveal that they are unsurpassed in both singability and poetic beauty; the singer need never apologize for them when used, as they should be before most English speaking audiences, instead of the original language.

A number of music publishers have kindly cooperated by permitting use of original copyrights in this edition. We wish to express our gratitude to them for their significant contribution in making possible the wide variety and attractive content of this song anthology.

Van A. Christy, Ph. D.
Professor of Music
University of California
Santa Barbara

Song Contents by Title

*Optional solo or duet

vii

*Optional duet or solo

Song Contents by Type

*Optional solo or duet

ix

*Optional duet or solo

x

I LOVE THEE

(Ich Liebe Dich)

Herrosee

Ludwig van Beethoven

English translation by Van A. Christy

Edited by Van A. Christy

I love but thee as thou dost me, At eve as on the mor - row, And
Ich lie - be dich, so wie du mich, am A - bend und am Mor - gen, noch

no day dawns for you and me But that we share its sor - row.
war kein Tag, wo du und ich nicht theil - ten un - sre Sor - gen;

Should all our way with ros - es bloom, And
Auch wa - ren sie für dich und mich ge -

1

sor - row nev-er___ trou - ble, Thy light-est tear I'd e'er re - move, And___
theilt, leicht zu er - tra - gen, du trös -te-test im Kum- mer mich, ich___

all___thy joy would dou - ble, Thy joy would dou -
weint'___in dei - ne Kla-gen, in dei - ne Kla -

ble. May___heav - en's bless-ing on thee fall, O thou, my life's fond
gen, d'rum___Got - tes Se- gen ü - ber dir, du mei - nes Le- bens

trea - sure; God___shel - ter thee what - e'er be-fall, And grant us love's___full___
Freu - de, Gott___schü - tze dich, er - halt' dich mir, schütz' und er- halt' uns___

STILL AS THE NIGHT

(Still wie die Nacht)

Carl Bohm

English version by Van A. Christy

Edited by Van A. Christy

Still as the night, deep as the sea,_____ Should be thy
Still wie die Nacht, *tief wie das Meer,_____* *soll dei - ne*

love_____ for me!_____ Still as the night,_____ and
Lie - be sein!_____ *Still wie die Nacht,_____ und*

deep as the sea, Thy love should be, thy love should be _____ for
tief wie das Meer soll dei - ne Lie - be, dei-ne Lie - be

me, _____ Thy love should be _____ for me.
sein, _____ soll dei - ne Lie - be sein!

When thou lov'st me _____
Wenn du mich liebst _____

as I love thee, _____ Then all thine own _____ I'll be.
so wie ich dich, _____ will ich dein ei - gen sein.

5

SONGS MY MOTHER TAUGHT ME

(Als die alte Mutter)

English version by Natalie MacFarren

Gypsy melody harmonized by Anton Dvorak

Edited by Van A. Christy

Songs my_____ moth - er_____
Als die_____ al - te_____

taught_____ me in the____ days long____ van -
Mut - ter mich noch____ lehr - te sin -

ish'd; Sel - dom from her eye - lids
gen, Thrä - nen in den wim - pern

were the tear - drops ban - ish'd.
gar so oft ihr hin - gen.

Now I ___ teach my ___
Jetzt, wo ich die ___

chil - - - - dren each mel - o - dious ___
Klei - nen sel - ber üb' im ___

meas - - - - - - ure;   Oft the tears____ are____
San - - - - - - *ge,*   *rie - selt's mir____ vom*

flow - - - - - - - - - ing,   Oft they flow____
Au - - - *ge,*   *rie - selt's oft____*

from my mem - ry's____ treas - ure.
von der brau - nen____ Wan - ge.

morendo

9

A RESOLVE

(Obstination)

English translation by Constance Bache

H. de Fontenailles

Edited by Van A. Christy

smile_____ and her smile._____
dieux,_____ des a - dieux,_____

It is all in vain to im - plore me
Vous au - rez beau faire et beau di - re,

All thought of her a - way to keep,
Dût el - le - mê - me l'i - gno - rer:
(him)

For still, al - though she may ig - nore me, I can
Je beux, fi - dèle a mon mar - ty - re, La pleu-
(he)

DEDICATION

(Widmung)

Wolfgang Müller

Robert Franz

*Translated by Arthur Westbrook

Edited by Van A. Christy

Andante (♩ = 50)

O, thank me not for what I sing thee; Thine are the songs, no gift of mine. Thou gav'st them me; I but re- turn thee What is and ev- er will be thine.

O dan - ke nicht für die - se Lie - der, mir ziemt es, dank - bar Dir zu sein; Du gabst sie mir, ich ge - be wie - der, was jetzt und einst und e - wig Dein.

14

OUT OF MY SOUL'S GREAT SADNESS

(Aus meinen grossen Schmerzen)

Heinrich Heine

Robert Franz, Op. 5, No. 1

*Translated by Frederic Field Bullard

Edited by Van A. Christy

ness.
zen.

They found her, and round her hov - ered, And
Sie fan - den den Weg zur Trau - ten, doch

now they've come back, and they scold me, And yet not a song - let has
kom - men sie wie - der und kla - gen, und kla - gen, und wol - len nicht

told ____ me What they in her heart dis - cov - - - - - -
sa - gen, was sie im Her - zen schau - -

ered.
ten.

I LOVE THEE

(Ich Liebe Dich)

(Jeg elsker dig)

From the Danish of Hans Christian Anderson

Edvard Grieg

English translation by Van A. Christy
German version by F. Von Holstein

Edited by Van A. Christy

Andante (♩ = 66)

1. Thou art my
1. Du mein Ge -

thoughts, my pur-est in-most be-ing,
dan - ke, du mein Sein und Wer- den!
lone my ev'-ry thought is burn-ing,
dein, kann stets nur dei-ner den- ken,

Thou, on-ly thou, my heart and
Du mein-es Her- zens er - ste
Pledged to thy good a-lone my
nur dei- nem Glück ist die - ses

soul a - dore.
Se - lia- keit!
love doth soar;
Herz ge - weiht;

Prized is thy love a-bove all earth-ly
Ich lie-be dich wie nichts auf die-ser
Wher'-e'er God wills my path in life be
wie Gott auch mag des Le-bens Schick-sal

17

see - ing,
Er - den,

I love thee, dear, I love thee, dear, I love thee, dear, and shall for
Ich lie-be dich, ich lie-be dich, ich lie-be dich in Zeit und

turn - ing,
len- ken,

ev - er more! I love thee, dear, and shall for ev - er more!
E -wig-keit! Ich lie-be dich in Zeit und E - wig-keit!

2. For thee a-
2. Ich den - ke

VERDANT MEADOWS

(Verdi prati, from "Alcina")

George Friedrick Handel

English text by Van A. Christy

*Arranged by Van A. Christy

Andante (♩= 76)

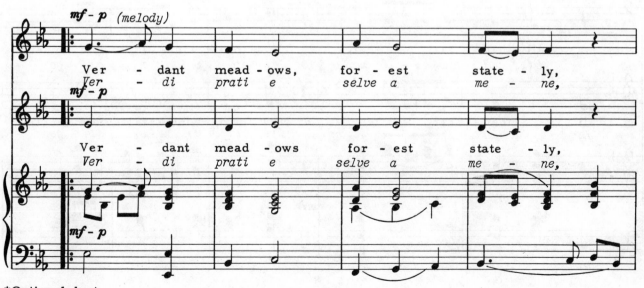

mf - p (melody)

Ver - dant mead - ows, for - est state - ly,
Ver - di prati e selve a me - ne,

Ver - dant mead - ows for - est state - ly,
Ver - di prati e selve a me - ne,

*Optional duet

19

fade. Ver - dant mead-ows, for - est state - ly,
rà. Ver - di prati e selve a - me - ne,

fade. Ver - dant mead-ows, for - est state - ly,
rà. Ver - di prati e selve a - me - ne,

Yield - ing — sooth-ing, wel - come shade.
Per - de — re - te la bel - tà.

Yield - ing — sooth-ing, wel - come shade.
Per - de — re - te la bel - tà.

Mag - ic
E can -

charm that now en - folds you, Will soon fade
gia - to il vago og - get - to, All' or - ror

21

when I a - gain be - hold__ you, In your cloak of snow ar - rayed,
del pri - mo a - spet-to, *Tut-to in voi ri - tor - ne - ra,*

In your cloak of snow ar - rayed,
Tut-to in voi ri - tor - ne - ra,

In your cloak of__ snow ar - rayed. Ver - dant
Tut - to in voi ri - tor - ne - ra, *Ver - di*

In your cloak of snow ar - rayed. Ver - dant
Tut - to in voi ri - tor - ne - ra, *Ver - di*

mead-ows, for - est state - ly, Yield - ing sooth-ing, wel - come
prati e selve a - me - ne, *Per - de - re - te la bel -*

mead-ows, for - est state - ly, Yield - ing sooth-ing, wel - come
prati e selve a - me - ne, *Per - de - re - te la bel -*

22

shade._____ Soon_____ 'neath win-ter's cold must fade._____
tà._____ Per - de - re - te la bel - tà._____

shade._____ Soon_____ 'neath win-ter's cold must fade._____
tà._____ Per - de - re - te la bel - tà._____

23

WHERE'ER YOU WALK

(Aria from "Semele")

George Friedrick Handel

Edited by Van A. Christy

24

*Lower text and phrasing as written originally, upper optional.

Very firmly the last time

to _____ a shade.

Wher - e'er you tread, the blush-ing flow'rs shall rise, And

all things flour-ish, And all things flour-ish, wher -

e'er you turn your eyes, wher-e'er you turn your eyes, wher-e'er you turn your eyes.

D.C. al Fine

SHE NEVER TOLD HER LOVE

Words by William Shakespeare
in "Twelfth Night"

Joseph Haydn

Edited by Van A. Christy

worm in the bud,

Feed on her dam - ask cheek.

She sat like pa - tience on a

mon - u - ment, Smil - ing, smil - ing at

grief,

Smil - ing, smil - ing at

grief.

29

SOMBRE WOODS

(Bois epais)

Music by Lully
Arr. by A. L.
*Edited by Van A. Christy

English version by Thoe. Marzials

Andante sostenuto ($\quad$ = 72)

Som - bre woods, ye glades dark and lone - ly,
Bois é - pais re - dou - ble ton om - bre,

Where mid - night gloom _____ en - ters on - ly, Oh!
Tu ne sau - rais être as - sez som - bre, Tu

your un - bound - ed night, If now this bro - ken
mal - heur - eux_____ a - mour, Je sens un dès - es

heart Ne - ver more may en - fold her,
poir Dont l'hor - reur est ex - trê - me,

If no more these eyes may be - hold her,
Je ne dois plus voir ce que j'ai - me,

Then ev - er more I hate the light, If
Je ne veux plus souf - frir le jour, Je

now this bro - ken heart Ne - ver more may en -
sens un dès - es - poir Dont l'hor reur est ex -

fold her, If no more these eyes may____ be -
trê - me, Je ne dois plus voir ce____ que

marcato

suivez la voix

hold her, Then ev - er more I hate the
j'ai - me, Je ne veux plus souf - frir le

light. _____
jour. _____

Piu mosso

33

THE SEA

Words by William Dean Howells

Music by Edward A. MacDowell, Op. 47, No. 7

Edited by Van A. Christy

mute, _____ And af -ter is e - vil cheer;_____

She shall stand on the shore____and cry in vain,

in vain, Man - y and man -y a year._____ But the

state -ly wide -winged ship lies wrecked, Lies wrecked on the un - known

THE JOYS OF LOVE

(Plaisir d'amour)

J. P. Clairs de Florian

Giovanni Martini

English version by Van A. Christy

Edited by Van A. Christy

Allegretto grazioso (♩. = 46)

The joys of love _____ so fleet-ing soon _ de-
Plai-sir d'a - mour _____ ne du - re qu'un _ mo-

part, _____ Leave sor - row all thro' _ life and a griev - ing
ment: _____ cha - grin d'a - mour du-re tout-te la vi -

*Piano score used by permission of G. Schirmer, Inc. Holders of the 1874 copyright.

37

part,_____ Leave sor - row all thro life and a_____
ment:_____ cha - grin d'a - mour du - re tou - te la -

griev - ing heart.
vi - e.

mf > *Piu mosso*

"Long as the brook - let shall
"Tant que cet - te eau - cou - le -

sweet - ly on - ward flow,_____ Thro' mead - ows rip - pling
ra _____ dou - ce - ment _____ vers ce ruis - seau qui

39

on its joy - ous path - way,   Thee   I   will
bor - de la - prai - ri - e   *je*   *t'ai - me -*

love.   now and for - ev - er all else a - bove.
rai,"   *me ré - pé - tait Syl - vi - e.*

Still   flows___the stream,_____ but chang'd is Syl - vio to-
L'eau   cou - le en - cor,_____ el - le a chan - ger pour-

(Syl - via)

day._____
tant._____
The
Plai -

DRINK TO ME ONLY WITH THINE EYES

(Old English Air)

Ben Jonson

*Col. R. Mellish

Edited by Van A. Christy

Very smoothly, and rather slow (♩. = 46)

Drink to me on - ly with thine eyes, And I will pledge with mine,

Or leave a kiss with-in the cup, And I'll not ask for wine; The

*This melody was sung by its composer, Col. R. Mellish, at the "Noblemen's and Gentle-men's Catch Club" of London. This club was founded in 1761, and included George IV and William IV among its early members. Some published editions list the song as an Old English Air.

thirst that from the soul doth rise, Doth ask a drink di-vine,

But might I of Jove's nec-tar sip, I would not change for

thine!

I sent thee late a ros-y wreath, Not so much hon'-ring thee

43

44

ON WINGS OF MUSIC

(Auf Flügeln des Gesanges)

Heinrich Heine

Felix Mendelssohn

**English translation anonymous

*Arranged by Van A. Christy

*May be sung as a duet for soprano and alto, tenor and alto, or tenor and baritone, or as a solo for high or medium voice.
**Used by permission of the Oliver Ditson Company, Bryn Mawr, Pa.

bloom - ing   On   banks by the Gan - ges___ tide.   Oh
sigh - ing   Fond   se - crets, like Fays   of the night.   The

there in   a   gar - den of   ros - es,   While moon-beams calm - ly
light-foot-ed   deer___ are   roam - ing   O'er crag and rock - y

shine, _____   The lo - tus flow'r___ un - clos - es   Her
steep, _____   While on,   in dis - tance gli - ding   The

calm - ly shine, The lo - tus flow'r___ un - clos - es   Her
rock - y steep, While on,   in dis - tance gli - ding   The

47

QUICK BREATH

cli - ning with thee while night gleams Un - der the spread - ing

3. Re - cli - ning with thee___while night gleams Un-der the

mf

palms; _____ We woo the pow'r___of bright dreams, To

spread-ing palms; We woo the pow'r___of dreams, To

cresc. *f*

shed their heav'n - ly charms, _____ To

cresc. *f*

shed their heav'n - ly charms, Their heav'n - ly charms, _____ To

cresc. *f* *cresc.*

49

LITTLE BOY BLUE

Words by Eugene Field

Ethelbert Nevin, Op. 12, No. 4

*Edited by Van A. Christy

*By permission of the Boston Music Co.

was when the lit-tle toy dog was new, And the sol-dier was pass - ing

fair:____ And that was the time when our lit-tle Boy Blue Kiss'd them, and put them

there.____ "Now don't you go till I come!" he said, "And don't you make an - y

noise," ___ So todd-ling off to his trun-dle bed,___ He dreamt of the pret - ty

53

PASSING BY

Edward Purcell

*Arranged by William Arms Fischer

* Edited by Van A. Christy

Robert Herrick

till   I   die.
till   I   die.

3. Cu -pid is wing - ed and doth range Her coun-try, so my

love_____doth change, But change the earth or change the sky, Yet

will I love her till I die.

*The high "f" and following downward portamento are optional for the more highly skilled singers.
55

FAITH IN SPRING

(Frühlingsglaube)

Ludwig Uhland

Franz Schubert

English translation anonymous

**Edited by Van A. Christy

Andante sostenuto (♪=84)

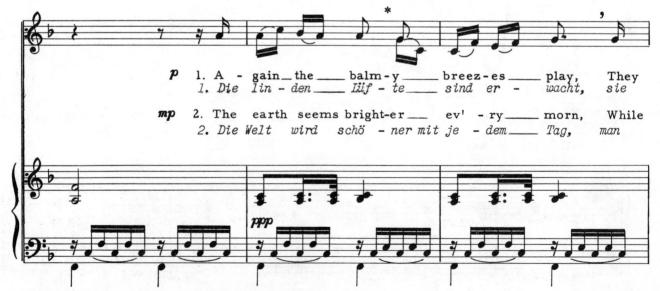

p 1. A - gain the balm-y breez-es play, They
1. Die lin - den Lüf - te sind er - wacht, sie

mp 2. The earth seems bright-er ev' - ry morn, While
2. Die Welt wird schö - ner mit je - dem Tag, man

*The upper note is for the first verse and the lower for the second where double stems occur.
**Used by permission of the Oliver Ditson Company, Bryn Mawr, Pa.

gen - tly___ mur - mur___ night and ___ day, And hea - ven's rich fra - grance
säu - seln und we - hen___ Tag und ___ Nacht, sie schaf - fen an al - len

blos - soms ___ gay ___ her robe ___ a - dorn, And fair - est flow'rs are
weiss ___ nicht ___ was noch ___ wer - den ___ mag, das Blu - hen will nicht

bor - row, ___ rich ___ fra - grance bor - row. New
En - den, ___ an ___ al - len En - den. O

bloom - ing, ___ and ___ flow'rs are bloom - ing: They
en - den, ___ es ___ will nicht En - den; es

sounds a - rise, and o - dors sweet, And
fri - scher ___ Duft, o neu - er Klang, O

bloom a - round in ev - 'ry vale, They bloom in
blüht das ___ fern - ste, tief - ste Thal, es blüht das

*The upper note is for the first verse and the lower for the second where double stems occur.

57

row.
den.

ing.

den.

pp-mf *a tempo*

2nd Verse

dim.

THE LOTUS FLOWER

(Die Lotusblume)

Heinrich Heine

Robert Schumann

Translation by Van A. Christy

Edited by Van A. Christy

The Lo - tus flow'r____ doth lan - guish
Die Lo - tus - blu - me äng - stigt

When the hot sun shines bright,
sich vor der Son - ne Pracht,

And with her droop - ing chal - ice She
und mit ge - senk - tem Haup - te er -

dreamily waits the cool night. The
wartet sie träumend die Nacht. Der

moon he is_____ her lov - er, He wakes her with fond__ de-
Mond, der ist_____ ihr Buh - le, er weckt sie mit sei - nem

light; For him her vir - gi - nal beau - ty Lies
Licht, und ihm ent- schlei-ert sie freund - lich ihr

fair in the qui - et of night. She
from - mes Blu - men - ge - sicht, Sie

THOU'RT LOVELY AS A FLOWER

(Du bist wie eine Blume)

Heinrich Heine

Robert Schumann, Op. 25, No. 24

*English translation Charles Fonteyn Manney

Edited by Van A. Christy

Thou'rt love - ly as a flow - er, So
Du bist_____ wie ei -ne Blu - me, so

fair and pure_____ thou art; I gaze on thee, and
hold und schön_____ und rein; Ich schau'dich an, und

sad - ness_____ Fills my de - vot - ed heart. My
Weh - muth_____ schleicht mir in's Herz hin- ein. Mir

hands_____ in ten-der de-vo-tion, I'd rest up-on_____ thy
ist,_____ als ob ich die Hän-de auf's Haupt dir le - gen

hair, Pray - ing that God ev-er keep thee
sollt', be - tend, das Gott dich er-hal-te

So love-ly pure and fair.
so rein und schön und hold.

THINK ON ME

Alicia Ann Scott

*Arranged by Van A. Christy

Moderato e molto sostenuto (♩ = 66)

1. When I no more be-hold thee, Think _____ on me.
2. In all thine hours of glad - ness,

By all thine eyes have told me, Think _____ on me. When hearts are
If e'er I soothed thy sad-ness, When foes are

light -est, When eyes are bright -est, When griefs are slight - est,
by thee, When woes are nigh thee, When friends all fly thee,

accel. *mf* *f*

Think on me,_____ Think _____ Oh think on

accel.

a tempo *rit.*

me,_____ Think, think on me.

a tempo *rit.* *a tempo* *rit.*

p *pp*

3. When thou hast none to cheer thee, Think__on me,

rit. *p* *pp*

66

When no fond heart is near thee, Think _____ on me, When lone - ly

sigh-ing, O'er plea - sure fly - ing, When hope is dy - ing,

Think on me, _____ Think _____ Oh think on

me, _____ Think, think on me. _____

THE LOST CHORD

Adelaide A. Procter

Arthur Sullivan

Edited by Van A. Christy

Seat-ed one day at the or - gan, I was wear-y and ill at ease, And my fin-gers wan-der'd i - dly O -ver the nois-y

keys; I know not what I was play-ing, Or what I was dream-ing then, But I

struck one chord of mu-sic Like the sound of a great A - men, like the sound of a

great_____ A - men. It

flood-ed the crim-son twi-light Like the close of an an - gel's Psalm, And it

69

lay on my fe-ver'd spir-it With a touch of __ in-fin-ite calm; It

qui-et-ed pain and sor-row Like love o-ver-com-ing strife, It

seem'd the har-mo-nious e - cho From our dis-cord-ant life. It

link'd all per-plex-ed mean-ings, In-to one per-fect peace, And

poco a poco più animato

trem-bled a-way in-to si-lence, As if it were loth to cease. I have

animando

agitato

sought, but I seek it vain-ly, That one lost chord di-vine, Which

came from the soul of the or-gan, And en-ter'd in-to

mine. It may be, that Death's bright an-gel Will

p cresc. molto ritard f Grandioso

speak in that chord a - gain; It may be, that on-ly in Heav'n I shall

hear that ___ grand A - men. It may be, that Death's bright an - gel Will

speak in that chord a - gain, It may be, that on-ly in Heav'n I shall

hear that grand A - men. ___

NONE BUT THE LONELY HEART

(Nur wer die Sehnsucht kennt)

Johann Wolfgang von Goethe

Piotr Ilyitch Tschaikovsky

Translated by Arthur Westbrook

Edited by Van A. Christy

None but the lone - ly heart
Nur wer die Sehn - sucht kennt,

Can know my sad - ness; _____ A - lone, and
weiss, was ich lei - de! _____ Al - lein und

part - ed far From joy and glad - ness.
ab - ge - trennt von al - ler Freu - de.

Heav'n's bound-less
Seh' ich an's

un poco marcato

arch I see Spread out a - bove ___ me. Ah! what a
Fir - ma- ment nach je - ner Sei - te. Ach! der mich

cresc.

dis - tance drear To one who loves ___ me!
liebt und kennt ist in der Wei - te.

From joy and glad-ness.
von al-ler Freu-de:

My sen-ses
Es schwin-delt

fail, _____ A burn-ing fire de-
mir, _____ *es brennt mein Ein - ge-*

vours me. None but the lone-ly heart Can
wei - de, *Nur wer die Sehn-sucht kennt, weiss,*

know my sad-ness.
was ich lei-de!

THE HOLY CITY

Words by F. E. Weatherly

Music by Stephen Adams

Edited by Van A. Christy

heard the chil-dren sing-ing, 'And ev - er as they sang, Me -
sun grew dark with mys - ter-y, The morn was cold and chill, As the

thought the voice of an - gels, From heav'n in an - swer rang, Me -
shad - ow of a cross a-rose, Up - on a lone - ly hill, As the

thought the voice of an - gels, From heav'n in an - swer
shad - ow of a cross a - rose, Up - on a lone - ly

rang. Je - ru - sa - lem, Je - ru - sa - lem,
hill. Je - ru - sa - lem, Je - ru - sa - lem,

Lift up your gates and sing,
Hark how the an - gels sing,

Ho - san - na in ___ the

high - est, Ho - san - na ___ to your King!

2. And

And once a - gain the scene was changed, New earth there seemed to ___ be, I

79

saw the Ho-ly Ci-ty Be-side the tide-less sea; The

light of God was on its street, The gates were o-pen wide, And

all who would might en-ter, And no one was de-

nied. No need of moon or stars by night, Or

BEAUTIFUL SAVIOR

(Crusaders' Hymn)

Anon. 19th Century

Silesian Folksong

Translation adapted by Van A. Christy

Arranged by Van A. Christy

Je - sus shines bright - er, Je - sus shines pur - er And
Je - sus is fair - er, Je - sus is pur - er, He

brings to all the world his love.
makes the sor - rowing spir - it sing.

3. Beau - ti - ful Sav - ior! Lord of all na - tions!

Son of ———— God and ———— Son of Man!

Glo - ry and hon - or, Praise, a - do - ra - tion, Now

and for ev - er more be Thine. Now

and for - ev - er more be Thine.

JOSHUA FIT THE BATTLE OF JERICHO

Traditional

*Spiritual arranged by Van A. Christy

Lyrics:
Josh-ua fit the bat-tle of ____ Jer-i - cho, ____ Jer-i - cho, ____ Jer-i - cho, ____ Josh-ua fit the bat-tle of ____ Jer-i - cho, And the walls come a-tum-blin' down. ____

*Portions of accompaniment from Chorus and Assembly,
copyright 1946 by Hall and McCreary Company. Used by permission.

Jer-i-cho,_____ Josh-ua fit the bat-tle of_____

Jer-i-cho, And the walls come a-tum-blin' down._____

Right up to the walls of Jer-i-cho, He marched with spear in

hand, "Go blow that ram horn", Josh-ua cried, "Cause the

battle am in my hand."____ And then the lamb, ram, sheep-horns be-

gin to blow, And the trumpet begins to sound,____

Joshua commanded the children to shout, And the

walls come a-tumblin' down. Hallelujah!

LONESOME VALLEY

White Spiritual

*Arranged by Van A. Christy

*Portions of accompaniment from Choral Adventures, copyright 1951 by Hall and McCreary Company. Used by permission.

*Optional ending.

BREAD OF ANGELS

(Panis angelicus)

César Franck

English text by Van A. Christy

*Arranged by Van A. Christy

High voice

O praise the Lord a-bove, Praise for His ho-ly love,

Low voice
Pa - nis an - ge-li-cus fit pa - nis ho-mi-num,

O praise the Lord a-bove, Praise for His ho-ly love,
Pa - nis an - ge-li-cus fit pa - nis ho-mi-num,

simile

*Optional duet or solo for medium or high voice.
Text from the Modern Choral Hour, copyright 1941 by Hall and McCreary Company.
Used by permission.

93

Optional ending by the arranger.

97

EYE HATH NOT SEEN

(From "The Holy City")

Alfred R. Gaul

Edited by Van A. Christy

God, which God hath pre - par'd ____ for them ____ that love Him, for

them ____ that love Him, the things which

God hath pre - par'd, pre - par'd for them that ____ love

piu mossc (♩ = 88)

Him.

99

things pre-par'd for them that love Him. There re-

main - eth there-fore a rest for the peo - ple, the

peo - ple of God; there - fore fear,

there - fore fear lest a - ny come

short _____ of it; there - fore fear, _____

_____ there - fore fear _____ lest a - ny come

short _____ of it, lest a - ny come short, come

short of it. _____ Eye hath not seen,

O REST IN THE LORD

(From "Elijah")

Felix Mendelssohn

Edited by Van A. Christy

give thee thy heart's de - sires. Com-mit thy way un - to Him, and trust in Him; com-mit thy way un - to Him, and trust in Him, and fret_ not thy-self _____ be-cause of e - vil - do - ers. O rest in the Lord, wait pa-tient-ly for Him, wait pa-tient-ly for Him; O rest in the Lord; wait pa-tient-ly for

A LEGEND

(Poem by Pleshtchéyeff after an English original)

*English version by Van A. Christy

P. Tchaikovsky, Op. 54, No. 5

Child Je-sus in His gar-den fair, Red ros-es grew that were His care. He wa-tered them with love each day,

To make them charm - ing, bright and gay. The ros - es blos - - som'd fair to see, When Ju - da's chil - dren rude and free, Tore ev - 'ry flow'r from branch - es there, And left the boughs all nude and bare.

"How wilt Thou weave Thy-self a crown, Now that the ros - es all are gone?" "The thorns are left," Child Je - sus said, _____ "The thorns are left to crown my head." So of the thorns a crown was made And

*Optional vocal ending not in the original.

LITHUANIAN SONG

(Lithauisches Lied)

Frederic Chopin

English version by Van A. Christy

*Edited by Van A. Christy

Allegro moderato (♩= 80)

Moderato ♩= 72

legatiss.

Clear was the morn - ing, the sun shone so bright - ly,
War schon frü - mor - gens ganz heim - lich im Tha - le;

Soft - ly the doves had be - gun their sweet coo - ing;
san - gen die Vög - lein auf Fel - dern und Hö - hen.

*Adapted from the translation of Steuart Wilson and used by permission of the Oxford University Press and G. Schirmer, Inc. 111

Scarce had I en - tered and sat me down light - ly,
Kaum bin ich heim und ich setz' mich zum Mah - le,

Then said my moth-er: "What have you been do - ing?
fragt mich die Mut - ter; "Was ist dir ge - sche - hen?

See how wet your hair and face! _____
Ei' ganz feucht sind Harr und Mie - der!"

Ah, I fear me sad dis - grace! _____
"Ach, mir fiel der Mut dar - nie - der."

wa - ter?"
grüss - en!"

"Ah me! Ah me! dear-est moth - er,
"Ach ja, ach ja, lie- be Mut - ter;

I will tell thee tru - ly, He begged so hard to see me bright and
will dir al - les sa - gen: Er hat - te mir so Vie - ler - lei zu -

ear - ly, Told me how he loved me,
kla - gen, sprach von sei - ner Lie - be

all his love re - call - ing, O moth-er! O moth-er!
im - mer im - mer wie - der: ach Mut - ter, O Mut - ter

some - how, _____ on my hair and cheeks, ' I
Thrä - nen _____ flos - sen reich - lich nie - der '

felt his tear-drops fall - ing. *Ah! _____
mir auf Haar und Mie - der!"* *Ach,*

Ah! _____
ach,

*Optional vocal ending by the editor.

115

THE OLD WOMAN AND THE PEDDLER

Traditional

English Folk-Ballad

Arranged by Van A. Christy

Allegretto (♩= 92)

There
was an old____wo - man, as I've heard tell,
When this lit - tle wo - man did first a - wake, Fa la

la la la la la,
She___went to mar - ket, her eggs for to sell,
She be - gan to shiv - er and be - gan to___shake,

name was Stout, Fa la la la la la la, — My
hope it be,

He — cut her pet-ti-coats round a-bout, Fa la
dog-gie at home — will sure know me;

la la la la la, And if it be I — he will wag his — tail,
He — cut her pet-ti-coats up to her knees,

Fa la la la la la la
Which made the old — wo-man to
— But if it be not, he will

shiv-er and sneeze,
bark and wail,
Fa la la la la la la."

5. Home went the old wo-man all in the dark, Fa la

la la la la la, Then up got her dog and be-gan to bark,

Fa la la la la la la, He be-gan to bark, and
she be-gan to cry, Fa la la la la la la,
"Lawk-a-mer-cy me, this is none of I! Boo-hoo-hoo!"
Fa la la la la la la.

A VERY COMMONPLACE STORY

(Ein sehr gewohnliche Geschichte)

Christian Felix Weisse

Joseph Haydn

English version by Van A. Christy

Edited by Van A. Christy

Allegretto staccato (♩=120)

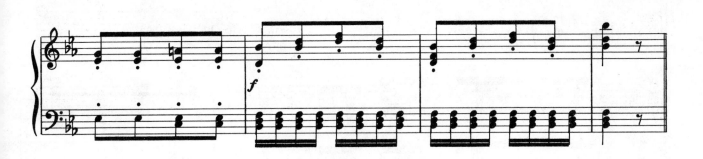

1. To Ba - bett's door Phi - lint came near; He knock'd and cried,"Is
1. *Phi - lint stand jüngst vor Ba - bett's Tür, und klopft' und rief; Ist*

3. But as he turned and would be gone, Most quick - ly was the
3. *Be - küm - mert will er wie - der gehn, da hort er schnell den*

"I ___ am Phi - lint; and ___ would not go." "No, ___
Ich ___ bin Phi - lent, lasst ___ mich hin - ein! Sie ___

He ___ hears, "A ti - ny ___ mo - ment stay, Be -
Er ___ hört: "Auf ein - en ___ Aug - en - blick, doch ___

no!" said ___ she, "No, no!"   2. He
kamm und ___ sprach: Nein, Nein!   2. *Er*

fore you ___ go a - way.   4. The
geh auch ___ gleich zu - rück!   4. *Die*

sighed and with the maid he begged, "But no," said she, "I
seufzt' und bat recht jam - mer - lich. Nein, sag - te sie, ich

pry - ing neigh - bors, far and near, Kept watch for him to
Nach - barn plagt die Neu - gier sehr; Sie war - te - ten der

am a - fraid, But no, "said she, "I am a - fraid, I
fürch - te dich! Nein sag - te sie, ich fürch - te dich! Ich

re - ap - pear, Kept watch for him to re - ap-pear, to
Wie - der - kehr, Sie war - te - ten der Wie - der - kehr, Der

am a - fraid, I am a - fraid? For
fürch - te dich! Ich fürch - te dich! Es

re - ap-pear, to re - ap - pear. He
Wie - der - kehr, der Wie - der - kehr. Er

night is here and I'm a - lone, Phi - lint, you must go
ist schon Nacht, ich bin al - lein, Phi - lent es kann nicht

came at last with morn - ing's light: They laughed with all their
kamm auch, doch ersts mor - gens früh, Ei, ei, wie lach - ten

124

*Optional ending by the editor for the last verse only.

A TRAGIC STORY

Wm. Makepeace Thackery

Wolfgang Amadeus Mozart

Edited by Van A. Christy

1. There liv'd a sage in days of yore, And he a hand-some
2. Says he, "The mys-ter-y I've found, I'll turn me round" he
3. And right, and left, and round a-bout, And up, and down, and

pig-tail wore; But won-der'd much, and sor-row'd more, Be-cause it hung be-
turn's him round; But still it hung be-hind____ him, But still it hung be-
in, and out He turn'd; but still the pig-tail stout hung stead-i-ly be-

hind him. He mused up - on this cur-ious__case, And swore he'd change the
hind him. Then round and_round, and out and_in, All day the puz - zled
hind him. And though his__ef - forts nev - er_slack, And though he twist and

pig-tail's place, And have it__hang-ing__at his face, Not dang-ling there be-
sage did spin; In vain it__mat-ter'd_not a pin The pig - tail hung be-
twirl and tack, A - las! still faith-ful__to his back, The pig - tail hangs be-

hind him, Not dang - ling there be - hind him.
hind him, The pig - tail hung be - hind him.
hind him, The pig - tail hangs be - hind him.

127

THE PRETTY CREATURE

Set by Stephen Storace

*Words & Music arranged by H. Lane Wilson

Edited by Van A. Christy

Oh! the pret-ty, pret-ty crea-ture! _____ When **I next __ **do ____ meet her, No __ more like a clown Will I face her frown, But

gal-lant-ly will I treat her,_____ But gal-lant-ly will I

treat her._____ Oh! the pret-ty, pret-ty, pret-ty, pret-ty, pret-ty

crea-ture,__Oh! the pret-ty, pret-ty, pret-ty, pret-ty crea-ture._____

But

more like a clown Will I face her frown, But gal-lant-ly will I

treat her,_____ But gal-lant-ly will I treat her._____

Oh! the pret-ty, pret-ty, pret-ty, pret-ty, pret-ty crea-ture, Oh!_____ the

pret-ty, pret-ty, pret-ty, pret-ty crea-ture._____

THE MILLER OF DEE

Traditional

17th Century English Tune adapted by
Van A. Christy from an arrangement for
three voices and string trio by Beethoven

Gaily, Vigorously (♩ = 92)

1. There was a jol-ly mil-ler once, lived on the riv-er
2. The rea-son why he was so blithe, he once did thus un-
3. I love my mill, she is to me Like pa-rent, child and

Dee; _____ He work'd and sang ___ from morn ___ to night, no ___
fold; _____ The bread I eat ___ my hands ___ have earn'd I ___
wife, _____ I would not change ___ my sta - - tion For ___

lark___ more blithe___ than he;___ *p* And__ this the bur - then
cov - et no___ man's gold;___ *p* I __ do not fear next
an - y oth - er in life;___ *f* Then__ push, push push the

of his song For - ev - - - er used to
quar - ter - day; In debt___ to none I
bowl, my boys, And pass___ it round to

be:_____ I care for no - bod - y
be:_____ I care for no - bod - y
me;_____ The long - er we___ sit

mf

no, not I, If___ no - bod - y cares___ for me.___
no, not I, If___ no - bod - y cares___ for me.___
here and drink, The__ mer - ri - er we___ shall be.___

FAR DOWN IN THE VALLEY

(Da unten im Tale)

German Folk Song Harmonized
by Johannes Brahms

English translation by Van A. Christy

Edited by Van A. Christy

1. Far down in the val-ley dark wa-ter doth creep,___ And I
1. Da___un-ten im Ta-le läufts Was-ser so trüb___ und i

can-not re-veal___ I loved thee so deep.
kann dirs nit sa-gen___ i hab di so lieb.

2. You___ prom-ised your
2. Sprichst all-weil von

love   and   faith - ful - ness   true,___   But a   lit - tle   of
Lieb,   *sprichst all - weil von*   *Treu___ und a   bis - se - le*

false - hood   I   found   was there   too.
Falsch-heit   is   au   wohl da - bei!

3. And if   ten   times   my   love   I pledge,
3. *Und___ wenn   i   dirs zehn - mal sag,*

o - ver and   o - ver,   You nev - er   can un-der-stand   why
dass   i   di   lieb,___ und du willst nit   ver - ste- hen   musz

I must be a ro - ver.
i halt weit-er gehn.

4. For the time when you loved me true, thank I thee
4. *Fur die Zeit, wo du g'liebt mi hast, dank i dir*

well,___ And I hope that an - oth-er's love your grief may dis-
schön,___ und i wünsch dasz dirs an- ders-wo bes - ser mag

pel.
gehn.

O CALM OF NIGHT

(In stiller Nacht)

English version by Van A. Christy

Suabian Folk Song arranged* by
Van A. Christy from the harmonization by Johannes Brahms

*Optional duet or solo for medium voice or high voice.

bor - row; No more we'll stray through mead - ows gay, I
wei - nen. Kein Vo - gel sang noch Freu - den klang man

bor - row; No more we'll stray through mead - ows gay, I
wei - nen. Kein Vo - gel sang noch Freu - den klang man

pass my days in weep - ing. For love I yearn; till
hö - ret in den Lüf - ten die wil - den tier traur'n

pass my days in weep - ing. For love I yearn; till
hö - ret in den Lüf - ten die wil - den tier traur'n

its re - turn My vig - il I'll be keep - ing.
auch mit mir in Stei - nen und in Klüf - ten.

its re - turn My vig - il I'll be keep - ing.
auch mit mir in Stei - nen und in Klüf - ten.

142

ALL THROUGH THE NIGHT

Text by Harold Boulton

Adapted by Van A. Christy

Old Welsh Air

Arranged by Van A. Christy

1. Sleep, my child, and peace at-tend thee All through the night;

Guard-ian an-gels God will send thee All through the night,

145

AWAY OVER YANDRO

(He's Gone Away)

Southern Mountain Tune

* Arranged by Van A. Christy

*Used by permission of Summy-Birchard Publishing Co.

*Yandro is a mountain.

BEGONE DULL CARE

Unknown

Old English

*Arranged by Van A. Christy

* Optional duet or solo for medium voice or low voice.

gone! dull care you and I __ shall nev-er a-gree. __

Be - gone dull care, _____ Long

And fain ____ thou would'st me

(melody)

time thou has been tar - r'ing here and fain ____ thou would'st me

kill, _____ But i' faith dull care, _____ Thou

kill, _____ But i' faith dull care, _____ Thou

nev-er shall have thy will.＿＿＿＿ 2. Too much

nev-er shall have thy will.＿＿＿＿

care＿＿＿＿＿＿＿＿ will make a young man＿turn gray,＿＿＿＿＿ And

2. Too much care,＿＿＿＿＿＿＿＿＿＿

too much care will turn an old man＿to

Too much care,＿＿＿＿＿＿＿

clay. _____ Gaily _____ So

My wife shall dance and I will sing, So

mer - ri - ly pass _____ the day, _____ For I hold it one of the

mer - ri - ly pass _____ the day, _____ For I hold it one of the

wise - est things To drive _____ dull care _____ a - way. _____ Be-

wise - est things To drive _____ dull care a - way. _____

(Repeat 1st verse faster) D.S.

(Repeat 1st verse faster) D.S.

154

MISTER BANJO

(Musieu Bainjo)

Creole Folk Song

Traditional text adapted by Van A. Christy

Arranged by Van A. Christy

Lively in staccato style of the banjo (♩ = 104)

Look at that dark-ey* play-in' the ban-jo, See all his fan-cy airs!

Look at that dark-ey play-in' the ban-jo, See all his fan-cy airs!

*If the word "darkey" is objectionable, use "dandy" instead.

1. Hat cock'd on so swank, Mis-ter Ban-jo, Walk-in' stick so lank, Mis-ter Ban-jo

Boots that go "crink crank" Mis-ter Ban-jo. Look at that dark-ey play-in' the ban-jo,

See all his fan-cy airs! Look at that dark-ey play-in' the ban-jo,

See all his fan-cy airs! 2. Red tie shin-in' bright, Mis-ter Ban-jo,

Hat as black as night, Mis-ter Ban-jo, Boots a tri - fle tight, Mis-ter Ban-jo.

Look at that dark-ey play-in' the ban-jo, See all his fan-cy airs!

Look at that dark-ey play-in' the ban-jo, See all his fan-cy airs!

3. Coat a pur-ple sight, Mis-ter Ban-jo, Spats a gleam-ing white, Mis-ter Ban-jo,

Socks a strip-ed fright, Mis-ter Ban-jo. Look at that dark-ey play-in' the ban-jo,

See all his fan-cy airs! Look at that dark-ey play-in' the ban-jo,

See all his fan-cy airs! See all his fan-cy airs!

See all his fan-cy airs! Mis-ter Ban-jo!

SHENANDOAH

(The Wide Missouri)

Traditional

*Chantey arranged by Van A. Christy

*Some authorities believe that this is a Missouri River Valley folk song and not a chantey.

TUTU MARAMBA

(Berceuse)

Brazilian Folk Song

English version by Van A. Christy

Arranged by Van A. Christy

*A mythical demon or bogey-man.

old arm-a-dill - o, the old__arm-a-dill - o, And spi-der so friend - ly will

watch from his nest; The old arm-a-dill - o, the old__arm-a-dill - o, And

spi - der so friend - ly will watch o'er your rest.

O my pret-ty lit - tle ba - by, moth-er's dar - ling child,

O my ti - ny lit - tle one, gen - tle sweet and mild;

O my pret - ty lit - tle ba - by, moth-er's dar-ling child,

O my ti - ny lit - tle one, gen - tle, sweet, and mild. Tu -

tu Ma - ram - ba shall nev - er harm my child, For

Suggestions for Interpretation

Style, tone color, and mood are given for each song as basic guides to expression. It must be understood that the following recommendations given in this regard are generalizations applying only to the prevailing style, tone color, and mood. Style seldom changes within a song, mood sometimes does temporarily, while tone color fluctuates considerably in some compositions to express word meaning and emotion most eloquently. Fluctuation of tone color occurs less frequently and does not vary as widely in classic literature as in romantic and modern music.

We must recognize, of course, that there is often more than one way to interpret a particular song beautifully. However, differences are normally in minor detail and not in the fundamentals of basic style, tone color, or mood. Unless a sound reason exists for change, it is advised that the following suggestions and the careful editing in the scores regarding interpretation be observed. They represent a carefully considered way and are valuable guides to success in effective interpretation.

ART SONGS

BEETHOVEN - I LOVE THEE (Ich liebe dich), p. 1

Style - Classic, lyric Bel Canto.
Tone color - Bright.
Mood - Deep and tender affection.

Beethoven's work bridged the Classic and Romantic periods. He is most famous as a composer of great symphonies but wrote a few songs, among which this is a favorite. It is distinctly in the classic style and is sung most effectively in lyric Bel Canto manner with however, somewhat greater tonal warmth and emotional intensity in the <u>forte</u> climax than typical of the purely classic idiom. A sustained tone line, easy, pure tone, clear diction, sincerity and depth of feeling are required to reveal the exquisite beauty of this song.

BOHM - STILL AS THE NIGHT (Still wie die Nacht), p. 4

Style - Sustained legato.
Tone color - Dark, rich.
Mood - Contemplation, deep affection.

This song is a universal favorite and one of the best studies to develop a sustained legato in a wide range of dynamics. Avoid dragging the tempo as often heard, keep the accompaniment smooth and flowing and the tone free, rich and suave in color. Especially take care that the faster <u>con moto</u> section is not slowed in tempo until the <u>ritard</u> is indicated in the score, since this anticipation weakens the effect of the final phrase.   Tone should be sonorous and rich in the final <u>fortissimo</u> climax and not bright, shrill or constricted as often heard.

DVORAK - SONGS MY MOTHER TAUGHT ME (Als die alte Mutter), p. 7

Style - Sustained lyric legato.
Tone color - Bright with mezzo intensity.
Mood - Reminiscent sad affection.

     "Songs My Mother Taught Me" is a universal favorite for Mother's Day as well as Dvorak's most popular concert song.   Particular care should be given to plaintive tone quality, significant portamentos, smooth dynamic variation and to accuracy and clarity of rhythm and intonation on the triplets and grace notes.   <u>Grace notes should not be omitted</u> or sung indefinitely as often heard.

FONTENAILLES - A RESOLVE (Obstination), p. 10

Style - Lyric legato.
Tone color - Bright, happy, except the ending.
Mood - Gay beginning, sad ending.

     French song literature offers few songs as easy and well adapted to the needs and abilities of beginning students as this straightforward and charming melody with the steady rhythmic syncopation in the accompaniment.   The first and second stanzas should move rather fast, slackening only at the end somewhat.   Ritardando should be greatest at the end of verse three and least at the end of verse two.   Dynamics are marked carefully for each verse.   On verse three employ a somewhat slower tempo as well as a darker tonal color.

FRANZ - DEDICATION (Widmung), p. 13

Style - Sustained lyric legato.
Tone color - Normal but with somewhat more mezzo quality and emotional intensity than usual.
Mood - Sincere gratitude.

     "Dedication" is Franz's most popular song and is sung often by concert artists either as part of a group or as an encore.   Rise and fall of melody in the phrase line and a most sensitive setting of the text make this one of the most beautiful melodies in the more simple type of art song literature.   It has few equals as a study song for beginning students. Start the second part somewhat faster and increase the emotional intensity of tone.   Observe the <u>pianissimo</u> carefully on the next to the last phrase in order to build effectively the <u>forte</u> climax following.   Do not hurry the tempo for this climax or for the ending phrase.

FRANZ - OUT OF MY SOUL'S GREAT SADNESS (Aus meinen grossen Schmerzen), p. 15

Style - Lyric legato.
Tone color - Dark.
Mood- - Sadness, grief.

     Like "Dedication," this song exemplifies Franz's ability to write a beautiful rising and falling tonal line within sufficient technical and range limitations to make it not only ideal study material but also a fine song for permanent repertoire.   Take care in the English translation that "sadness" does not become "sadnuss," "gladness" become "gladnuss"; that the "ing" in "singing" and "winging" is not sung as "in"; and that "r" in "birds", "heart," "her," "hovered" and "discovered" is not growlingly anticipated.   This is an ideal song in which to conquer these fundamental diction problems that afflict most students.

GRIEG - I LOVE THEE (jeg elsker dig), p. 17

Style - Lyric legato
Tone color - Normal to bright.
Mood - Reminiscent to passionate fervor at climax.

     This song should always be sung in a good English translation before English audiences rather than in German, as often heard, since neither language is the original. Although the same in title as Beethoven's "I Love Thee," p. 1, the two songs are totally different in style and mood content; one is typically Classic, the other typically Romantic. "I Love Thee" is Grieg's most popular song and is widely sung in concert, radio, and for weddings. It develops a passionate intensity in the forte climax few songs can equal. The song should begin quietly, tenderly and reminiscently, gradually increasing fervor and dynamics as indicated. The phrase, "I love thee, dear," should start softly, a tempo, and gradually crescendo in successive waves of crescendo-diminuendo to the climax. A gradual increase in tempo through this passage also assists in building a more powerful climax. The ritard should be very slight at the climax for the first verse and very broad for the second. Piano accompaniment should be played legato with the introduction, in particular, demanding a smooth tonal flow and no ritard or the passing harsh dissonances will be too unpleasant.

HANDEL - VERDANT MEADOWS (Verdi prati, from "Alcina"), p. 19

Style - Sustained legato
Tone color - Warmer and richer than normal.
Mood - Quiet contemplation.

Many of Handel's early works and operas were written to Italian texts. However, "Verdant Meadows" is usually sung in its English translation today. Besides being a lovely concert number, it is easy in range and phrasing requirements and is unsurpassed for teaching sustained legato style. When sung in English it is also excellent in teaching proper enunciation of the ugly "er" syllable. Tempo should be unhurried and steady. The "A" section requires a warmer, richer mezzo tone and a slower tempo than the contrasting sections. At no time should dynamics be permitted to be really loud.

HANDEL - WHERE'ER YOU WALK (Aria from "Semele"), p. 24

Style - Lyric legato with some florid passages, classic idiom.
Tone color - Somewhat brighter than normal.
Mood - Quiet, contemplative, deep affection.

Although not native born, Handel spent most of his life in England and is ranked as her greatest composer. He wrote many operas which were popular at the time but it is his genius in oratorio upon which his fame rests today. However, many of Handel's arias from opera have survived as favorite concert songs, among which "Where'er You Walk" is outstanding. It should be sung with a steady tempo in the Classic style, quiet dignity and deep but restrained emotional fervor. The contrasting "B" section should be taken at a somewhat faster tempo and louder dynamics with the "A" section returning reminiscently pianissimo and building up a stronger climax to the fine.

HAYDN - SHE NEVER TOLD HER LOVE, p. 27

Style - Lyric legato.
Tone color - Normal.
Mood - Gentle tragedy.

Haydn did not always adhere strictly to "Classic Form" in his songs. Some, like this, anticipate the later "Romantic" Art Song in that they are completely free in structure and may be sung with more emotional intensity than the typical Classic Period song allows. This text by William Shakespeare provides the best loved of Haydn's several songs set originally to English texts. It is straightforward and not difficult for the beginning student but requires flexible finger technic for the piano interludes. Vocal interpretation should reflect the picture of the courageous miss who never spoke of her secret love but "put on a brave front," smiling at her hidden grief. Narrative style and normal tone color employed at the beginning should become more dramatic and intense in emotional quality at the end, but by no means should be carried to the extent appropriate to the later German Leider. In the last phrase, "Smiling, smiling at grief," use bright tone quality on the first "smiling" (marked forte), and darker mezzo quality for the piano remainder of the phrase. Be sure to articulate the word "grief" clearly.

LULLY - SOMBRE WOODS (Bois Epais, from "Amadis"), p. 30

Style - Sustained legato.
Tone color - Dark.
Mood - Reflection, intense sadness.

Lully's opera, "Amadis" is long since forgotten but the aria, "Bois Epais," and its various English versions, is heard frequently in concert. It is neither difficult in range or length of phrase and may be done effectively by even beginning students if optional breaths are taken where indicated and the tempo increased somewhat faster than ideal. This song provides the student with a fine melody as well as an interesting exercise for developing steady breath control in sostenuto style and for stimulating the production of a suave, sonorous, dark tone color.

MACDOWELL - THE SEA, p. 34.

Style - Dramatic sostenuto.
Tone color - Dark.
Mood - Tragic.

Edward MacDowell is often listed as the greatest American composer. "The Sea" is one of his best songs. It offers excellent study material for the vocal student, providing in a limited range a great variety of dynamics and serving as an excellent introduction to dramatic style in singing. Effective rendition requires a sombre tonal color, sostenuto style and command of a wide range of dynamics. Dark tone color will be difficult for the student in this song for certain words; "sea", "evil", "cheer", "deep", and "asleep". A rounded lip "oo" position on these bright vowel words will be found necessary to obtain the required solemnity of tone. More than normal accent on primary beats, a pronounced rhythmic swing and careful attention to word emphasis and tonal inflection is required. Except for the broad <u>ritard</u> at the end there is a tendency by most singers to take the tempo of this song too slowly.

MARTINI - THE JOYS OF LOVE (Plaisir d'amour), p. 37.

Style - Sustained lyric legato.
Tone color - Normal.
Mood - Complaint over faithless love.

This favorite concert song of the Classic Period must be sung with the grace, delicacy, restraint, steadiness of tempo and pure lyric tone typical of the Bel Canto style. Tempo changes should be between rather than within sections. The piano part must be played with light, lyric delicacy and is not easy. This song has long been a favorite in the concert repertoire as well as an outstanding song for teaching purposes.

MELLISH - DRINK TO ME ONLY WITH THINE EYES (Old English), p. 42.

Style - Lyric legato.
Tone color - Normal.
Mood - Quiet, tender affection.

Although composed, "Drink to Me Only with Thine Eyes," like many of Stephen Foster's songs, has become a favorite folk song of the people. It should be sung simply and tenderly with sustained lyricism and no suggestion of bombastic dynamics. Many experienced vocal teachers rank this song number one for assignment to beginning students. It has a fine text and a lovely rise and fall of melodic line.

MENDELSSOHN - ON WINGS OF MUSIC (Auf Flügeln des Gesanges), p. 45.

Style - Lyric legato.
Tone color - Bright.
Mood - Quiet and gentle love.

"On Wings of Music" is so well known as to need very little comment. Audiences love it while tenors and sopranos, in particular, find it most grateful as a lyric study and concert song. It will be found equally effective as a solo or a duet.

NEVIN - LITTLE BOY BLUE, p. 50.

Style - Lyric legato.
Tone color - Bright.
Mood - Sad reminiscence, tenderness.

Ethelbert Nevin had much in common with Stephen Foster in his gift for folk-like melody. A number of his compositions became well known with "The Rosary" being the most famous. "Little Boy Blue" is a sentimental song of a quasi-ballad type, a favorite with audiences and usually sung by tenors or sopranos. It is easy to sing effectively if it isn't over-sentimentalized but sung simply and phrased musically with pure plaintive tone and flowing lyric style.

PURCELL - PASSING BY, p. 54.

Style - Lyric legato.
Tone color - Bright.
Mood - Abiding love, affection.

This popular love song is not by the great English composer, Henry Purcell, as many assume, but by a later composer. It should be sung with maximum lyricism in style with a clear Bel Canto tone. Interesting artistic variety is provided if the three verses are sung with the dynamics and phrased as indicated in the editing of the score. An optional fifth line high "f" sung <u>pianissimo</u> (ppp) on the last phrase furnishes an excellent exercise to develop high <u>pianissimo</u> technic. Dynamic climax should be achieved at the end of verse two on the word "her." At this point make the <u>fermata</u> longer than on verse one and do not <u>diminuendo</u>. If it can be done naturally and not sound forced or overdone, take an audible gasp-breath ("Caruso Grunt") at the end of this hold to further emphasize the dynamic and emotional climax. The third verse sung <u>pianissimo</u> both at the beginning and end should give a reverent quality more effective here than louder dynamics could possibly be. Observe the tricky change of phrasing at the beginning of verse three. This is one of the author's favorite teaching songs for helping beginning students obtain a foundation in lyric legato style and drill in the mastery of basic diction. The word "her" occurs many times and must always be sung "huh---r." Be sure not to anticipate the "r" also in the word "heart" and to sing the two words "cupid" and "winged" as they should sound and not "cu-pud" and "wing-ud" as nearly all amateurs do.

SCHUBERT - FAITH IN SPRING (Frühlingsglaube), p. 56.

Style - Lyric legato with some florid phrases.
Tone color - Normal but with more emotional intensity than usual.
Mood - Joy in nature; hope and faith in change for the morrow.

"Faith in Spring" furnishes an introduction to some of the more difficult songs in Song Anthology, Volume II, which require greater vocal flexibility. It is an excellent example of Schubert's unsurpassed flowing melodic lyricism. Although not easy, the accompaniment is not as difficult as it appears when taken at the slow tempo intended with a count of 4/8 in the measure. Numerous portamentos and the two turns should be executed gracefully and cleanly. The two phrases in which the turns occur furnish ideal drill material for the student to master this florid device; they should be transposed upward and downward in all comfortable keys. This song demands a classic grace and delicacy in phrasing. Any effort at dramatics or heavy handed dynamics will spoil the effect. Although there are a few contrasting phrases, remember that the overall effect of this song should be that of joy and optimism.

SCHUMANN - THE LOTUS FLOWER (Die Lotusblume), p. 60.

Style - Lyric sostenuto.
Tone color - Somewhat warmer and richer than normal.
Mood - Quiet mystical tenderness.

This lovely song should reflect the mystical exotic quality of the Lotus Flower, the peace and beauty of moonlight, and the tender and ecstatic love of the flower and the moon. It is not a dramatic or tragic song but has a somewhat tragic allegorical suggestion in the last phrase. It should be sung with calm repose, maximum beauty of warm tone and delicacy of sentiment.   Tonal color should have a shimmering brilliance on the <u>pianissimo</u> phrase, "The moon, he is her lover." Follow the dynamic and tempo markings carefully in building the <u>forte</u> climax but do not sing too loudly or with a shrill "white tone." The last phrase should be sung with considerable <u>ritard</u> and end softly.

SCHUMANN - THOU'RT LOVELY AS A FLOWER (Du bist wie eine Blume), p.63.

Style - Lyric legato.
Tone color - Normal but with a somewhat more mellow quality in places.
Mood - Deep and tender affection.

The original text by Heine has been set to music by many composers.   Many authorities rank this Schumann setting as one of the most beautiful short art songs in existance with Rubinstein's version of the same poem ranked a close second.   Phrasing should be smoothly legato and sustained with the voice expressing a quiet and reflective but happy mood. Do not breathe at the end of measure seven unless necessary.

SCOTT - THINK ON ME, p. 65.

Style - Lyric sostenuto.
Tone color - Bright, plaintive.
Mood - Tender reflection of deep and abiding love.

As a lyric love song of folk-like character, Alicia Ann Scott's melody and text of "Think On Me" has few equals for lovely vocal line, simplicity and tender sentiment.   It should be sung with an intense plaintive tone and a supremely flowing sostenuto.   Singers should have little trouble in interpretation of dynamics and phrasing if they follow the carefully marked score.   This song is a universal favorite with both students and audiences.

SULLIVAN - THE LOST CHORD, p. 68.

Style - Sustained legato.
Tone color - Somewhat darker than normal.
Mood - Quiet reminiscence; exaltation at the end.

Sullivan is said to be the most gifted of native English composers.   Most famous for his inimitable comic operas, he seldom turned his attention to other types of composition. "The Lost Chord" is best known among his few songs.   It is an audience favorite and unsurpassed as a study song for developing sostenuto breath control.   Beware of taking the beginning tempo too slowly and of letting the tempo drag in quiet sections as often heard.   Sing repeated notes as sostenuto as possible.

TSCHAIKOVSKY - NONE BUT THE LONELY HEART (Nur wer die sehnsucht kennt), p. 73.

Style - Sustained legato.
Tone color - Bright.
Mood - Deep melancholy.

This great and very popular song has few if any peers in intensity of feeling and tragic mood.   As often interpreted, it suffers from a too sentimental dragging of the tempo, depriving expression of intensity of emotion and weakening the powerfully moving climax indicated by the composer.   Starting at the phrase, "Alone, and parted far", both tempo and dynamics should increase to the climax which does not end with the voice but with a following measure of crashing <u>fortissimo</u> for the piano.   In order to heighten suspense, the quarter rest following this climax should be extended to two or three beats before the voice enters in anguished <u>pianissimo</u>, "My senses fail." An audible gasp catch-breath ("Caruso Grunt") is a most powerful emotional effect after "fail" for the singer that can do it naturally without affectation.   The last phrase should be sung with slower tempo, very sostenuto, and with intense sorrow.

SACRED SONGS AND SPIRITUALS

ADAM - THE HOLY CITY, p. 77.

Style - Lyric legato.
Tone color - Somewhat brighter than normal.
Mood - Religious exhaltation.

Stephen Adams composed a number of sacred songs which are still popular in religious services today; among these "The Holy City" is considered the best. Opinion of critics vary as to its greatness. However, there is little doubt about its forthrightness, sincerity and melodic charm even if the originality of accompaniment and harmonization is not the equal of master art songs. It is easy and furnishes not only a fine medium for study purposes in developing lyric technic but is also a well liked repertoire number appropriate to most church services. Tempo should be kept moving, the story of the text emphasized, and a rather bright tone and lyric style used. An exception to the bright tone is found only on the parts beginning "And once again the scene was changed," where a darker and more dramatic tone is most effective up to the return of the cantabile section.

CHRISTY (Arr.) - BEAUTIFUL SAVIOR (Crusader's Hymn), p. 83.

Style - Sustained legato.
Tone color - Dark mezzo.
Mood - Worship, adoration, reflection, abiding faith.

This beautiful Silesian folk song has been a favorite melody in Christian churches for centuries. It should be sung with great sincerity, deep religious fervor, nobility of expression, richness of tone, and flowing sostenuto. The accompaniment must also observe the maximum of singing sostenuto style, avoiding any tendency toward percussive pounding on the climaxes.

CHRISTY (Arr.) - JOSHUA FIT THE BATTLE OF JERICHO (Spiritual), p. 86.

Style - Narrative, with both lyric and dramatic technic required.
Tone color - Normal to bright.
Mood - Excited militant exultation and religious fervor.

It would be difficult or impossible to find any spiritual of a more exciting militant character or one with a stronger and more interesting rhythm. Whether or not one believes the story of the text or considers it merely an exciting fable, we can all agree that this is musically one of the most outstanding spirituals of its type for solo singing. Tempo must be kept moving and rapid, primary accents and syncopations stressed and the dramatic character of the text delivered without reserve. It should end with great emotional fervor, making the portamento at the end on "Oh Lord" very strong and pronounced.

CHRISTY (Arr.) - LONESOME VALLEY (White Spiritual), p. 91.

Style - Sustained legato.
Tone color - Leaning toward dark.
Mood - Sadness, resignation.

This lovely spiritual is in complete contrast to the previous "Joshua Fit the Battle of Jericho." It should be sung very sostenuto with steady walking tempo, quietly and with restrained emotion. On the climactic cry, "Oh," emotion is released with a crescendo and brighter tone quality.

FRANCK - BREAD OF ANGELS (Panis angelicus), p. 93.

Style - Sustained legato.
Tone color - Bright.
Mood - Exalted veneration.

César Franck was known as a mystic and an intensely religious man whose character was reflected in the music he wrote. "Panis Angelicus" is without doubt one of the most sincere, devout and lovely sacred songs ever composed. It is equally effective as a solo or in the duet arrangement provided. Tone production should be exceptionally free, clear, flowing and beautiful to express the lofty sentiment of the text. There must be no "shrieking" quality of the voice on the forte climax.

GAUL - EYE HATH NOT SEEN (From "The Holy City"), p. 98.

Style - Sustained legato.
Tone color - "A" section dark mezzo, contrasting sections normal to bright.
Mood - Quiet worship in section "A"; first contrasting section joyous exultation; second con-
    trasting section fear.

This air from the popular cantata, "The Holy City," is a universal favorite for sacred services and is often heard in concert. The "A" section should be sung with quiet intensity and dark tonal color, the first contrasting section with normal color to express the narrative character of the text, and the second contrasting section with varied tonal color to express the shifting dramatic content of the text. The last return of the "A" section may well be somewhat softer than the initial statement to good effect.

MENDELSSOHN - O REST IN THE LORD (From "Elijah"), p. 104.

Style - Sustained legato.
Tone color - Dark mezzo.
Mood - Abiding veneration and trust.

Mendelssohn's great oratorios are his outstanding contribution to the art of music. Next to Handel's "Messiah," "The Elijah," from which this aria is taken is the most beloved of all oratorios. "Oh Rest in the Lord" is as earnest an expression of deep religious faith as can be found in all vocal literature. It is too well known to require extensive comment. For best effect it must be sung with quiet, dignified religious fervor and a suave, rich tone with careful attention to sostenuto and finesse in phrasing.

TSCHAIKOVSKY - A LEGEND, p. 107.

Style - Lyric legato.
Tone color - Normal to bright.
Mood - Sadness, grief.

This narrative story about the childhood of Jesus foretelling his later death on the cross should be sung with sustained emotional intensity and a tonal quality appropriate to the text's tragic significance. Starting with plain narrative style and normal tone color, the voice should gradually increase in poignancy of meaning as the allegorical story unfolds. The last page should be sung very sostenuto with steady control of the two long <u>crescendo</u> phrases indicated.

BALLADS

CHOPIN - LITHUANIAN SONG (Lithauisches Lied), p. 111.

Style - Narrative lyric legato.
Tone color - Bright in the text for the girl's voice, dark for the mother's voice.
Mood - Varied - plain narrative style in the beginning; mother's part, suspicion and angry ac-
    cusation; daughter's part, happiness and exaltation at the end.

This gem among folk ballads deserves more frequent programming by concert artists in the United States. It has humor and a plaintive Gypsy-like character. Tone should be harsh and accusing when the mother exclaims <u>fortissimo</u>, "I know that story," and somewhat aspirate and threatening when repeating the same phrase piano following. It is of utmost importance to project the dramatic meaning of the text with clear-cut diction and appropriate tonal color and accent. Although tempo should be flexible, care should be taken that the general pace does not drag.

CHRISTY (Arr.) - THE OLD WOMAN AND THE PEDDLER (English folk-ballad), p. 116.

Style - Narrative lyric legato.
Tone color - Normal.
Mood - Humorous.

This delightfully humorous English ballad should be sung with sprightly tempo, precise articulation and clear tone quality. The typical "fa la" should be sung more softly than the story which it interrupts frequently. Much of the charm is lost unless the ideas and humor of the story are made entirely clear to the listener. Verse five requires a slower beginning tempo with softer dynamics and a darker tone quality but a return to even faster tempo and louder dynamics than elsewhere at the tempo primo energico sign. The last five measures should be quite deliberate and marcato in style of accent.

HAYDN - A VERY COMMONPLACE STORY (Ein sehr gewohnliche Geschichte), p. 121.

Style - Narrative.
Tone color - Normal.
Mood - Humorous.

Although pious and unusually serious, "Papa Haydn" also had a keen, earthy, and at times, waggish sense of humor as is clearly evident in the "Surprise Symphony" and in this and other songs. Sing this song in straightforward narrative ballad style with particular attention to clear-cut articulation, word emphasis and projection of the meaning, humor, and somewhat risque flavor of the denoument in the text.

MOZART - A TRAGIC STORY, p. 126.

Style - Narrative lyric legato.
Tone color - Normal.
Mood - Humorous.

Thackery's amusing tale, about the sage who unsuccessfully attempted to maneuver his pig-tail so that it would hang in front instead of behind, set to music by Mozart furnishes a good easy humorous ballad or encore. Straightforward narrative delivery, steady animated tempo and plain articulation are necessary for effective expression. It is a good study song to develop clear articulation and project a humorous text.

WILSON (Arr.) - THE PRETTY CREATURE (Old English), p. 128.

Style - Light accented.
Tone color - Bright.
Mood - Gay admiration.

This gay and clever old English ballad is a delightful concert song often heard sung by male singers or as part of an Old English group sung by either sex. It is an unsurpassed study song for all voices in learning crisp articulation, portamento and flexible phrasing. Tempo should be at a lively pace except where indicated otherwise in the score. This song must be obviously enjoyed by the singer in order to be effective. Expression of the face should be animated and interpretation should be in such a manner that the personal feelings of the smitten swain are revealed clearly.

FOLK SONGS

BEETHOVEN-CHRISTY (Arr.) - THE MILLER OF DEE (17th Century English Tune), p. 134.

Style - Dramatic accented robusto.
Tone color - Darkly masculine.
Mood - Vigorous jollity, conviviality.

This is a man's song especially well suited in style and tone color to the powerful bass or dramatic baritone voice. It is recommended for initial review and study by all voices, female as well as male, as a means of becoming acquainted in an easy song with one of the essential styles and tone color required at times in the more difficult examples of German Lieder, opera, and contemporary art songs. Tone must be spacious, sonorous and dark, while effect of manly vigor must be maintained even in soft passages. The first and second verses are robusto narrative style with vigorous dynamics; the third verse starts quietly in a reflective mood but changes to an even more vigorous robusto style than verse one on the words "Then push, push, push the bowl my boys," which should be half-shouted in a vigorous convivial manner.

BRAHMS - FAR DOWN IN THE VALLEY (Da unten im Tale, German Folk), p. 136.

Style - Lyric legato.
Tone color - Normal.
Mood - Regretful reflection.

This fine lyric German folk song harmonized by Brahms tells the story of a rover whose wanderlust was stronger than his love. It is very easy in range, straightforward, and should present little interpretive difficulty to the student if directions in the score are followed.

BRAHMS-CHRISTY (Arr.) - O CALM OF NIGHT (In stiller Nacht, Suabian Folk Song), p. 139.

Style - Sustained legato.
Tone color - Dark.
Mood - Sombre, intense sorrow.

Brahms was so intrigued by this lovely German folk song that he arranged it for both solo voice and vocal quintet. It should be sung very sostenuto and with greater emotional intensity than characteristic of most sad folk songs. Tonal color on the approach and at the forte climax should be brighter. As an optional duet, in this arrangement, it is quite effective for soprano and alto, or for tenor and alto.

CHRISTY (Arr.) - ALL THROUGH THE NIGHT (Welsh Air), p. 143.

Style - Sustained legato.
Tone color - Dark.
Mood - Contemplative, quiet grieving love.

This beautiful Old Welsh Air is a favorite of concert artists. It requires a dark, mellow tone, rather slow tempo, sustained legato, quiet dynamics and tender sentiment. A finer study song would be difficult to find for the beginning student. The "B" section of each verse should be faster in tempo while tone color should change to bright in the second verse at the text, "Joy will come to thee at morning." The extremely sad third verse is often omitted in other publications; here it is included as optional.

CHRISTY (Arr.) - AWAY OVER YANDRO (Southern Mountain Tune), p. 147.

Style - Lyric legato.
Tone color - Dark in the refrain, normal in the verses.
Mood - Sad reflection.

"Away Over Yandro" is unsurpassed by any of the numerous Southern Mountain folk songs. Its plaintive modal melody, shifting meter and interesting text combine to make it an excellent concert repertoire number in this arrangement. Clear diction, lyric legato style, good tone and sincerity without affectation or over-sentimentality are required for effective rendition.

CHRISTY (Arr.) - BEGONE DULL CARE (Old English), p. 151.

Style - Light accented.
Tone color - Bright.
Mood - Gay

This Old English song should be sung with a gay, bouncing lilt. Forceful, crisp articulation is a "must" and, unlike legato lyric style, the ending consonant may be anticipated frequently to the advantage of interpretation. Verse one (repeated as verse three) should start accented and be contrasted in the "B" section with a more lyric legato style, while verse two should reverse these styles as well as the dynamics in the sections mentioned. An effective duet arrangement is optional.

CHRISTY (Arr.) - MISTER BANJO (Musieu Bainjo, Creole Folk Song), p. 155.

Style - Light accented lyric.
Tone color - Bright.
Mood - Gay and humorous.

The light staccato banjo-type accompaniment provided, the humerous description of the ridiculously foppish dandy, the attractive melody and infectious rhythm all combine to make "Mister Banjo" a folk song that should be a favorite with both students and audiences. It should be sung with especially precise articulation with care to proper word accent in an animated narrative style. The accompanist should imagine the sound of a banjo and emulate it as closely as possible.

CHRISTY (Arr.) - SHENANDOAH (Chantey), p. 159.

Style - Sustained legato.
Tone color - Dark and mellow.
Mood - Nostalgic reminiscence, longing for home.

Most authorities classify "Shenandoah" as a chantey while others claim that it is really a Missouri and Mississippi River folk song. In any case, its nostalgic and beautiful melody and shifting meter make it a unique and lovely song for solo voice or ensemble singing. It is, without a doubt, one of the finest American folk tunes. It is suggested that the song be started quietly and that each verse mount gradually in intensity to <u>forte</u> on the fourth and last verse. Tone should be dark, sustained and always suggestive of deep longing for home. Keep tempo steady with only a slight <u>ritard</u> at the end of each verse, broadening considerably for the last verse.

CHRISTY (Arr.) - TUTU MARAMBA (Brazilian Folk Song), p. 161.

Style - Lyric legato.
Tone color - Varied.
Mood - Quiet, gentle assurance.

We know of no more beautiful, varied and musically interesting folk lullaby than "Tutu Maramba." It should be sung with free and beautiful tone, gentle rocking rhythm, never loudly, and ended of course, very softly. For best expression sing the "A" and "B" sections with a dark and rich tone quality and the "C" section with normal to bright quality.

Suggestions for Prounciation

*HINTS ON ITALIAN PRONUNCIATION

Vowels

Every vowel must be pronounced distinctly in Italian; none can be omitted or slighted when two or more vowel sounds are included under one note, as is often the case. There are no dipthongs in Italian. When two or more vowels occur together, stress is placed on the principal one, the others being rapidly but distinctly sounded. Vowel stress is often indicated in modern editing. In such frequently encountered combinations as ai, eu, oi, and iei, every vowel must be pronounced distinctly. Generally speaking, Italian vowels are pronounced by the better educated natives with a very free open tone. When the Italian sings or recites poetry he seems to taste and enjoy every vowel, while quickly and distinctly articulating the consonants in order that the vowel may be savored longer.

A vowel is generally open (long) when the syllable is closed, i, e., ends in a consonant, e. g., for-za, per-fet-te; closed (short) when the syllable is open, i. e., ends in a vowel, e. g., do-lo-re, o-no-re. When singing use the first pronunciation of vowels listed below if in doubt and until authoritative information can be secured. The "Pronouncing Guide to French, German, Italian and Spanish" by Jones, Smith and Walls lists many words used by the singer and should be of considerable assistance to the beginner. A good standard dictionary in the language being sung is more comprehensive as well as providing the exact meaning of words being sung, a necessity for really convincing diction. Students wishing to sing well in a foreign tongue are urged to first obtain a good English translation of the song; second, to look up the pronunciation and meaning of all words; and third, to read the foreign language over dramatically several times as a necessary preliminary key to effective interpretation, just as they should if singing the song in English.

a   like English ah in father, never like a in name or ball, e. g., ama = ah-mah, amor = ah-mor.

e   usually like e in the English word they, or like ay in day without the vanishing ee, e. g., pera = pay-rah, cena = chay-nah.
sometimes short as e in pen, e. g., mensa = men-sah, pessimo = pes-see-moh.

i   usually like the English ee in bee, e. g., iddio = ee-dee-oh, fine = fee-nay.
sometimes short like i in him, e. g., finire = fi-ni-ray, stringendo = strin-gen-doh.

---

*These hints are offered as an aid to beginners and are generalizations covering most problems; they are not to be interpreted as an exhaustive set of rules.

o usually like the English exclamation <u>oh</u> without the vanishing <u>oo</u>, e. g., corte = koh-rtay, popolo = poh-poh-loh.
  sometimes like <u>o</u> in <u>off</u>, e. g., collo = kaw-loh, sotto = saw-toh.

u like <u>oo</u> in <u>moon</u>, e. g., futuro = foo-too-roh, uomo = oo-oh-moh.

Consonants

Hard consonants are in general pronounced more softly than in English; soft consonants with great delicacy. The rolled <u>r</u> is difficult for English speaking pupils as they confuse it with a gutteral sound whereas the Italian articulates it with a quick tip of the tongue "flutter" as the tongue is brought in juxtaposition with the upper teeth. A good word to use in developing this skill is <u>tredice</u> (tray-deece).

<u>b</u>, <u>d</u>, <u>f</u>, <u>l</u>, <u>n</u>, <u>p</u>, <u>q</u>, are pronounced as in English.

<u>c</u> before <u>a</u>, <u>o</u>, and <u>u</u>, and before consonants has the sound of k, e. g., <u>carro</u>, <u>corso</u>, <u>culto</u>, <u>creta</u>; before <u>e</u>, <u>i</u>, and <u>y</u> it has the sound of <u>ch</u> in the word <u>church</u>, e. g., <u>cera</u>, <u>citta</u>.

<u>cc</u> before <u>e</u>, <u>i</u>, or <u>y</u> like <u>ch</u>, e. g., <u>eccellenza</u>, <u>cerdiccio</u>.

<u>ch</u> before <u>e</u> or <u>i</u>, like <u>k</u>, e. g., <u>occhio</u>, <u>chiesa</u>.

<u>g</u> before a, o, or u and before consonants, like g in <u>God</u>, e. g., <u>gallo</u>, <u>gola</u>, <u>grande</u>; before <u>e</u> or i like <u>j</u> or soft as in <u>gem</u>, e. g., <u>genero</u>, <u>giro</u>.

<u>gg</u> before <u>e</u> and i like <u>ddsh</u>, e. g., <u>corraggio</u>, <u>reggente</u>.

<u>h</u> is invariably silent.

<u>j</u> when used as a vowel, like Italian <u>i</u>; as a consonant, like <u>y</u> in <u>young</u>.

<u>r</u> as in English, at the end of words or syllables or in combination with another consonant, but shriller and more rolling.

<u>sce</u>, <u>sco</u>, <u>scu</u> like <u>skay</u>, <u>ski</u>, <u>skoo</u>, e. g., <u>scala</u>, <u>scoria</u>, <u>scudo</u>.

<u>sce</u>, <u>sci</u>, like <u>shay</u> and <u>she</u>, e. g., <u>scelta</u>, <u>scimmia</u>.

<u>z</u> soft, like <u>ds</u> as in <u>zelo</u>, <u>manzo</u>.
  sharp, like <u>ts</u> as in <u>zio</u>, <u>forza</u>.

Supplementary Examples of Consonant Pronunciation

<u>c</u>	before <u>a</u>	like <u>kah</u>,	e. g., <u>cane</u> = kah-ne
	before <u>o</u>	like <u>ko</u>,	e. g., <u>coda</u> = ko-da
	before <u>u</u>	like <u>koo</u>,	e. g., <u>cuculo</u> = koo-koo-lo
	before <u>e</u>	like <u>chay</u>,	e. g., <u>cece</u> = chay-chay
	before <u>i</u>	like <u>chee</u>,	e. g., <u>bacino</u> = ba-chee-no
<u>cc</u>	before <u>e</u>	like <u>ttsche</u>,	e. g., <u>accento</u> = a-ttshen-to
	before <u>i</u>	like <u>ttshee</u>,	e. g., <u>occidente</u> = o-ttshee-den-te
<u>ch</u>	before <u>e</u>	like <u>kay</u>,	e. g., <u>amiche</u> = ah-mee-kay
	before <u>i</u>	like <u>kee</u>,	e. g., <u>occhio</u> = ok-kee-o
<u>ci</u>	before <u>a</u>	like <u>chah</u>,	e. g., <u>baciamento</u> = bah-chah-main-to
	before <u>o</u>	like <u>cho</u>,	e. g., <u>cacio</u> = cah-cho
	before <u>u</u>	like <u>chew</u>,	e. g., <u>ciurmare</u> = chewr-mah-ray
<u>gh</u>	before <u>e</u>	like <u>ghey</u>,	e. g., <u>gorghetto</u> = gor-ghey-to
	before <u>i</u>	like <u>ghee</u>,	e. g., <u>ghiro</u> = ghee-ro

<u>gi</u>	before <u>a</u>	like <u>jah</u>,	e. g., <u>giardino</u> = jahr-dee-no
	before <u>o</u>	like <u>jo</u>,	e. g., <u>giocoso</u> = jo-co-so
	before <u>u</u>	like <u>joo</u>,	e. g., <u>giubbilo</u> = joob-bee-lo
<u>gl</u>	before <u>ia</u>	like <u>l'yah</u>,	e. g., <u>battaglia</u> = baht-tah-l'yah
	before <u>ie</u>	like <u>l'yey</u>,	e. g., <u>biglietto</u> = beel-l'yey-to
	before <u>io</u>	like <u>l'yo</u>,	e. g., <u>foglio</u> = fol-l'yo
	before <u>iu</u>	like <u>l'yoo</u>,	e. g., <u>pagliuca</u> = pah-l'yoo-kah
<u>gn</u>	before <u>a</u>	like <u>n'yah</u>,	e. g., <u>vigna</u> = veen-yah
	before <u>o</u>	like <u>n'yo</u>,	e. g., <u>legno</u> = len-yo
	before <u>u</u>	like <u>n'yoo</u>,	e. g., <u>ignudo</u> = een-yoo-do
	before <u>e</u>	like <u>n'yay</u>,	e. g., <u>igneo</u> = een-yay-o
	before <u>i</u>	like <u>n'yee</u>,	e. g., <u>ogni</u> = ohn-yee
<u>sch</u>	before <u>e</u>	like <u>skay</u>,	e. g., <u>schema</u> = skay-mah
	before <u>i</u>	like <u>skee</u>,	e. g., <u>maschio</u> = mah-skee-o
<u>sci</u>	before <u>a</u>	like <u>shah</u>,	e. g., <u>sciarpa</u> = shar-pah
	before <u>o</u>	like <u>sho</u>,	e. g., <u>sciolto</u> = shol-to
	before <u>u</u>	like <u>shoo</u>,	e. g., <u>sciupare</u> = shoo-pah-ray

*HINTS ON GERMAN PRONUNCIATION

German articulation and enunciation are much more forceful than that of infor-mal English, having a more accented gutteral quality. The consonants, in particular, must be far more energetic than in English. The principal accent generally falls on the first syl-lable or, after prefixes, on the syllable following the prefix.

The "Pronouncing Guide to French, German, Italian and Spanish" by Jones, Smith and Walls lists many words used by the singer and should be of considerable assistance to the beginner. A good standard dictionary in the language being sung is more comprehensive as well as providing the exact meaning of words being sung, a necessity for really convincing diction. Students wishing to sing well in a foreign tongue are urged to first obtain a good English translation of the song; second, to look up the pronunciation and meaning of all words; and third, to read the foreign language over dramatically several times as a neces-sary preliminary key to effective interpretation, just as they should if singing the song in English.

Vowels and Dipthongs

The umlaut ö and ü in German have no counterpart in English but are paralleled by the <u>eu</u> and the <u>u</u> in French. For the German ö and the French <u>eu</u> the lips are rounded into the <u>oh</u> position, the base of the tongue raised into the <u>ay</u> position and a vowel sound between the English <u>oh</u> and <u>ay</u> is sounded. For the German ü and the French <u>u</u>, the lips are rounded into the <u>oo</u> position, the base of the tongue raised into the <u>ee</u> position and a vowel sound be-tween <u>oo</u> and <u>ee</u> is sounded. The German <u>ü</u> leans more toward the <u>oo</u> while the French <u>u</u> is nearer <u>ee</u>.

<u>a</u>   always like <u>ah</u> in <u>father</u>, e. g., <u>Abend</u> = ah-bunt, aber = ah-bur.

ä   like <u>ay</u> before <u>h</u> and any single consonant, e. g., ähnlich = ayn-likh, Häfen = hay-fun. otherwise like <u>e</u> in bed, e. g., Kämme = kehm-muh, ändern = ehn-durn.

ae   pronounced the same as ä, e. g., Aether = ay-tur, Aeste = ehs-tuh.

ai   like <u>i</u> in <u>sigh</u>, e. g., haide = high-duh, Mai = my.

---

*These hints are offered as an aid to beginners and are generalizations covering most problems; they are not to be interpreted as an exhaustive set of rules.

au   like <u>ow</u> in <u>how</u>, e.g., Hauch = howkh, Auge = ow-guh.

e   like <u>uh</u> when final and in unstressed initial syllables, e.g., Liebe = lee-buh, getan = guh-tahn.
like <u>u</u> in inflectional endings except <u>e</u> and in unstressed non-initial syllables, e.g., Nebel = nay-bul, wegen = vay-gun.
like <u>ĕ</u> in <u>set</u> (except those mentioned first above) for prefixes, e.g., erlauben = ehr-low-bun, ergaben = ehr-gay-bun.
like <u>ay</u> in accented syllables, before <u>h</u>, before a single consonant, and when doubled, e.g, eher = ay-ur, jeder = yay-dur, Meer = mayr.
like <u>eh</u> when followed by two consonants, e.g., Eltern = ehl-turn, vergessen = fehr-gehs-sun.

ei   like <u>i</u> in <u>sigh</u>, e.g., ein = eign, einsam = ein-zahm

eu   like <u>oy</u> in <u>boy</u>, e.g., feurig = foy-rikh, euch = oykh.

i   like <u>i</u> in <u>sit</u> as a rule, e.g., Himmel = him-mul, immer = im-mur.
like <u>ee</u> before <u>h</u> and in <u>dir</u>, <u>Lid</u>, <u>mir</u>, <u>wir</u> and <u>wider</u>, e.g., ihm = eem, dir = deer.

ie   like <u>ee</u> usually, e.g., Knie = knee, lieber = lee-bur.
sometimes like <u>i</u> in <u>sit</u>, e.g., vierzig = fir-tsikh, viertel = fir-tell.

o   like <u>oh</u> when before a single consonant, before <u>h</u>, and when final or doubled, e.g., Forelle = foh-rel-luh, rot = roht.
otherwise like <u>aw</u>, e.g., Dorf = dawrf, Gott = gawt.

ö   like <u>ay</u> with modification of <u>oh</u> position (Note: See introductory paragraph) before <u>h</u> and and before a single consonant, e.g., böse = bay-zuh, öde = ay-duh, Höhe = hay-uh.
like <u>ĕ</u> in <u>set</u> elsewhere, e.g., öffnet = ehf-nut, Glöcklein = glehk-lighn.

oe   like <u>ö</u>.

u   like <u>oo</u> before a single consonant and before h, e.g., Hut = hoot, Blume = bloo-muh.
otherwise like <u>u</u> in butter, e.g., Mutter = mut-tur, Mund = munt.

ü   like <u>ee</u> with modification of <u>oo</u> position (Note: See introductory paragraph) before <u>h</u> and before a single consonant, e.g., verglühen = fehr-glee-un, trüber = tree-bur.
elsewhere short like <u>i</u> in a round lip position, e.g., müssen = mis-sun, Fürstin = fir-stin.

ue   like <u>ü</u>.

Consonants

<u>f</u>, <u>h</u>, <u>k</u>, <u>l</u>, <u>m</u>, <u>p</u> and <u>t</u> like English.

b   like English when beginning a word or syllable.
like <u>p</u> when the last letter of a word before a voiceless consonant such as <u>f</u> or <u>k</u> and in the prefix <u>ab</u>, e.g., stab = stahp, abgehen = ahp-gay-un.

c   like <u>ts</u> before <u>ä</u>, <u>e</u>, <u>i</u>, <u>ö</u>, and <u>y</u>, e.g., Cent = tsehnt.
like <u>k</u> elsewhere, e.g., Cour = koor.

ch   There is no comparable sound in English for the "front" <u>ch</u> and the "back" <u>ch</u>. In the front <u>ch</u> in such words as <u>dich</u>, <u>ich</u>, the tongue is arched upward with the tip resting easily against the lower front teeth, while the <u>ch</u> is produced with a sound somewhat like a hiss; in the back <u>ch</u> in such words as <u>lachen</u>, <u>machen</u>, the tongue is arched highly at the back toward the soft palate and as the tongue and palate come into close proximity, air is hissed through the opening.
like <u>k</u> before an <u>s</u>, e.g., fuchs = fooks, and in words of Greek origin before <u>a</u>, <u>o</u>, <u>l</u>, or <u>r</u>, e.g., Christ = krist.
like <u>kh</u> in such words as Milch = milkh, Loch = lawkh.

ck like kk, e.g., schrecken = shrehk-kun.

d like English when beginning a word or syllable.
  like t when the last letter of a word, and before a voiceless consonant, e.g., Lied = leet,
  Mädchen = mayt-khun.

g like English at the beginning of a syllable or word.
  like kh in the ending ig, e.g., König = kay-nikh.
  like k when final and before a consonant, e.g., klug = klook, Magd = mahkt.

h like h in English, but is silent when final.

j like y, e.g., ja = yah, jeder = yay-dur.

n like n in English as a rule.
  like ng before k, e.g., schenken = shehng-kun.

q like kv, e.g., Quell = kvell.

r always like the trilled r in English.

s like English s when doubled, between a voiceless consonant and a following vowel, and
  when final, e.g., besser = behs-sur, Achsel = ahk-sul, als = ahls.
  like z before a vowel at the beginning of a word, between vowels, and between a voiced
  consonant and a following vowel, e.g., sanft = zahnft, Nase = na-zuh, emsig = ehm-zikh.
  like sh before p and t at the beginning of a word, e.g., Spiele = shpee-luh, stand =
  shtahnt.

sch like sh, e.g., schlug = shlook, Scheiden = shi-dun.

th like t, e.g., thun = toon.

v normally like f, e.g., Vater = fah-tur, viel = feel.
  like v in words of foreign origin, e.g., Klavier = klah-veer.

w like v. e.g., was = vahs, Walt = vahlt.

x like ks, e.g., Hexe = Hehk-suh.

y like ee, e.g., Cypresse = tsee-prehs-suh.

z like ts, e.g., zu = tsoo, zart = tsahrt.

*HINTS ON FRENCH PRONUNCIATION

French is a much more nasal language than Italian, German or English and is excellent for helping to correct voices that have a tendency to be too breathy or gutteral in production. The nasal vowels have no English equivalents. They are enunciated by saying the vowel and at the same time allowing some breath to escape through the nose and not by the inclusion of the m, n, or ng as is sometimes erroniously assumed. French vowels should usually be nasalized as described if there is a single m or n in the same syllable following the vowel, but if m or n preceeds the vowel, or is doubled, or if mn occurs, there is usually no nasality in production.

Sounds of the French language should be formed with greater precision, vigor, clarity and suavity than is common in informal English. Vowels should be uniform through-out their utterance without any dipthongization characteristic of English. Therefore, the student should be careful not to change tongue or lip position once the vowel is formed.

_____

*These hints are offered as an aid to beginners and are generalizations covering most problems; they are not to be interpreted as an exhaustive set of rules.

French differs also from English, Italian and German in that all syllables normally have uniform or nearly equal stress. While the final _e_ is silent in French speech, it is often used by composers in songs as a final syllable, in which case it is given the sound of uh.

The "Pronouncing Guide to French, German, Italian and Spanish" by Jones, Smith, and Walls lists many words used by the singer and should be of considerable assistance to the beginner. A good standard dictionary in the language being sung is more comprehensive as well as providing the exact meaning of words being sung, a necessity for really convincing diction. Students wishing to sing well in a foreign tongue are urged to first obtain a good English translation of the song; second, to look up the pronunciation and meaning of all words; and third, to read the foreign language over several times dramatically as a necessary preliminary key to effective interpretation, just as they should if singing the song in English.

Vowels

_a_ and _à_   like _a_ in path or somewhat broader, e.g., ami = a-mee, canard = ka-nar.
    like _ah_ when preceeding a final _s_, e.g., bas = bah, cas = kah.
    like _ah_ nasalized* when followed by _m_, _n_, or _ng_, e.g., ambre = ahbr, errant = eh-rah.

_â_   usually like _ah_, e.g., château = shah-toh, relâche = ruh-lahsh.

_ai_ and _aî_   like _ĕ_ in met, e.g., esprit = ehs-pree, *airain = eh-reh.

_au_   like _oh_ usually, e.g., aussi = oh-see, berceau = behr-soh.

_e_   (mute) like _uh_, e.g., petit = puh-teet, cerise = suh-reez, or silent when final, e.g., plaine = plehn, and cerise (above).

_é_   (acute) like _a_ in day, e.g., école = ay-kohl, équipée = ay-kip-ay.

_è_   (grave) like _ĕ_ in set, e.g., excèss = ek-seh, guère = gehr.

_ê_   (circumflex) like _e_ in sĕt, e.g., fête = feht, rêver = reh-vay.

_i_   nearly always as ee, e.g., livre = lee-vr, vie = vee.
    usually like _y_ when preceeding another vowel, e.g., grenier = gruh-nyay.
    like _eh_ when nasalized by a following _m_ or _n_, e.g., *festin = fehs-teh, *important = eh-pawr-tah.

_o_   usually like _aw_, e.g., coloré = kay-law-ray, *montrer = maw-tray.
    like _oh_ when the last sound of a word, e.g., Pierrot = pyeh-roh, chose = shohz, and before _s_, e.g., oser = oh-zay, rosier = roh-zyay.

_ô_   (circumflex) like _oh_, e.g., môtif = moh-teef, nôtre = nohtr.

oeu   like _ay_ in the _oh_ position, e.g., boeux = bay, voeu = vay.
    like _eh_ in the _aw_ position, e.g., oeuf = ehf.

_oi_   usually like _wa_, e.g., courtois = koor-twa, choir = shwar.
    like _weh_ when nasalized by a following _n_, e.g., *foin = fweh, *loin = lweh.

_ou_   usually like _oo_, e.g., bouquet = boo-key, nouveau = noo-voy.
    like _w_ when before another vowel, e.g., grenouille = gruh-nweey, oui = wee.

_u_   usually like _ee_ nasalized in the _oo_ position, e.g., rue = ree, superbe = see-pehrb. (Note: See discussion of the French _u_ and German _ü_ on p. 187)
    like _y_ when followed by a vowel, e.g., muable = my-abl, nuages = nyazh.
    like _uh_ when made nasal by a following _m_ or _n_, e.g., humble = uhbl, chacun = sha-kuh.

---

*See first paragraph for description of nasality of vowels when followed by n, m, or ng.

b   usually like b in English.
like p before c, s, and t, e. g., absent = ap-sah, obtenir = awp-tuh-neer.

c   usually like k, e. g., cache = kash, coer = kehr.
like s before e, i, and y, e. g., celle = sehl, ciel = syehl, and when cedilla is indicated, e. g., garçon = gahr-saw.

cc   pronounce the first c hard and the other soft when followed by e, i, or y, e. g., accident = ak-see-dah, success = syk-say.

d   usually like d in English.
like t when linked, e. g., prendil = prah-teel.

f   like f in English.

g   nearly always as g, e. g., glisser = glee-say.
like zh before e, i, and y, e. g., gage = gazh, agir = a-zheer.

gg   pronounce the first g hard and the other soft when followed by e, i, or y, e. g., suggérer = syg-jay-ray.

gn   usually like ny, e. g., règne = reh-ny.

h   usually silent.
sometimes aspirate h in words of Teutonic origin, e. g., hâler = hah-lay.

j   like zh, e. g., je = zhuh, jambe = zhahb.

k   like k in English.

l   usually like l in English.

m   usually like m in English except when silent*if preceeding another consonant, e. g., trompette = traw-peht.

n   usually like m in English except it is silent *when final or before another consonant, e.g. maman = mah-mah, confier = kaw-fyay.

p   like p in English

ph   like f in English, e. g., philosophe = fee-law-zawf, phare = far.

q and qu like k, e. g., cinq = sehk, quel = kehl.

r   like r in English.

s   usually like s in English, e. g., Sabbath = sah-bah, savoir = sa-vwar.
like z between vowels, e. g., désir = day-zeer, désert = day-zehr.
like z when linked, e. g., ignobles entraves = ee-nyaw-bluh zah-trav.

ss   always like s in English.

t   usually like t in English, e. g., tableux = ta-bloh.
like s in terminations having ti followed by a vowel, e. g., nation = nah-seeaw, action = ak-seeaw. (Exceptions: adjectives and nouns ending in tier have the normal t sound, e. g., sortie = sawr-tee.

th   like t in English, e. g., thé = tay, thème = tehm.

---

*However, it causes the preceeding vowel to be nasal.

<u>v</u>   like <u>v</u> in English.

<u>w</u>   normally not in French except in words from a foreign source where it is pronounced as <u>v</u>, e. g., valkyrie = vahl-kee-ree, wagon = va-gaw.

<u>x</u>   like <u>ks</u> before a consonant and between vowels, e. g., exprimer = eks-pree-may, oxygene = awk-see-zehn.
like <u>k</u> before <u>ce</u> and <u>ci</u>, e. g., excellent = ek-seh-lah.
like <u>gz</u> after <u>e</u> and preceeding a vowel, e. g., exalter = ayg-zal-tay.

<u>y</u>   usually like <u>y</u> before a vowel, e. g., payer = peh-yay, pays = pay-ee.
sometimes like a vowel, e. g., mystere = mee-stayr, martyr = mahr-teer, symbol = seh-bawl, thym = teem.

<u>z</u>   like <u>z</u> in English.

NOTES

NOTES

NOTES

NOTES

NOTES

NOTES

NOTES

NOTES

NOTES

NOTES

NOTES

NOTES

NOTES

NOTES